Violin Music the Whole World Loves

*39 popular melodies
arranged for violin and piano
in the first position
for easy sight-reading
and
amusement in the home*

By

C. Paul Herfurth

and

Edward Strietel

THE WILLIS MUSIC COMPANY

America, the Beautiful

VIOLIN

Tune "Materna" by
SAMUEL A. WARD
Arr. by C. Paul Herfurth

Aria
from the Opera "Der Freischütz"

VIOLIN

CARL MARIA VON WEBER
(1786-1826)
Arr. by C. Paul Herfurth

Adeste Fideles

VIOLIN

Portuguese **Hymn**
Arr. by EDWARD STRIETEL

W. M. Co. 5744-Comp.

Annie Laurie
(Scotch Tune)

VIOLIN

LADY JOHN SCOTT
(1847)
Arr. by EDWARD STRIETEL

Auld Lang Syne

VIOLIN

Scotch Folk-song
Arr. by EDWARD STRIETEL

Battle Hymn of the Republic

VIOLIN

Arr. by EDWARD STRIETEL

Written about 1855 by
WILLIAM STEFFE
A Southern composer of Sunday School Songs

W. M. Co. 5744-Comp.

Beautiful Dreamer

VIOLIN

STEPHEN C. FOSTER
(1826-1864)
Arr. by C. Paul Herfurth

Beautiful Heaven
(Cielito Lindo)

VIOLIN

Mexican Folk-song
Arr. by C. Paul Herfurth

Carry Me Back to Old Virginny

VIOLIN

JAMES A. BLAND
Arr. by C. Paul Herfurth

Columbia, the Gem of the Ocean

VIOLIN

English Melody
Arr. by EDWARD STRIETEL

V. M. Co. 5744-Comp.

Come back to Erin

VIOLIN

CLARIBEL
CHARLOTTE ARLINGTON BARNARD
(1830-1869)
Arr. by EDWARD STRIETEL

W. M. Co. 5744 - Comp.

Comin' thro' the Rye

(Scotch Air)

VIOLIN

Arr. by EDWARD STRIETEL

W. M. Co. 5744 - Comp. *Copyright, MCMXIX, by The Willis Music Company*

Dixie Land
(Song of the Confederacy)

Written in 1859 for a minstrel show by
DAN D. EMMETT
(1815-1904)
Arr. by EDWARD STRIETEL

VIOLIN

W. M. Co. 5744-Comp.

Hail, Columbia

(Written during the threatened war with France in 1798)

VIOLIN

Attributed to PHILIP PYLE(_ 1793)
Arr. by EDWARD STRIETEL

The Heart Bowed Down
from "The Bohemian Girl"

MICH. Wm BALFE
(1808-1870)
Arr. by EDWARD STRIETEL

VIOLIN

W.M.Co.5744-Comp.

Home on the Range

VIOLIN

Cowboy Song
Arr. by C. Paul Herfurth

Home, Sweet Home

HENRY R. BISHOP
(1786-1855)
Arr. by EDWARD STRIETEL

VIOLIN

W. M. Co. 5744 - Comp

Juanita*

VIOLIN

Old Spanish Melody
Arr. by EDWARD STRIETEL

* Prnounced, Wa-neé-tah

W. M. Co. 5744 - Comp

'Tis the last Rose of Summer
(Irish Air)

Melody used by
Fried. Flotow in the opera "Martha"
Arr. by EDWARD STRIETEL

VIOLIN

W. M. Co. 5744 - Comp

Listen to the Mocking-Bird

ALICE HAWTHORNE
pseudonym for Septimus Winner
Arr. by EDWARD STRIETEL

VIOLIN

Lorelei

VIOLIN

FRIEDRICH SILCHER
(1789-1860)
Arr. by EDWARD STRIETEL

W. M. Co. 5744-Comp.

Long, Long Ago

VIOLIN

THOMAS H. BAYLY
(1797- 1839)
Arr. by C. Paul Herfurth

Marseillaise

French National Anthem

VIOLIN

Written for Luckner's Army
as it marched on the Tuileries
Aug. 10, 1792

ROUGET DE LISLE

Arr. by EDWARD STRIETEL

Massa's in de Cold, Cold Ground

STEPHEN C. FOSTER
(1826-1864)
Arr. by EDWARD STRIETEL

VIOLIN

Copyright, MCMXIV, by The Willis Music Company

My Country, 'tis of Thee

First sung publicly at a children's celebration
of American Independence, Boston, July, 4, 1852

VIOLIN

HENRY CAREY (1685-1743)
Arr. by EDWARD STRIETEL

My Old Kentucky Home

VIOLIN

STEPHEN C. FOSTER
(1826-1864)
Arr. by EDWARD STRIETEL

Old Black Joe

STEPHEN C. FOSTER
(1826-1864)
Arr. by EDWARD STRIETEL

VIOLIN

W. M. Co. 5744 - Comp.

The Old Folks at Home

STEPHEN C. FOSTER
(1826-1864)
Arr. by EDWARD STRIETEL

VIOLIN

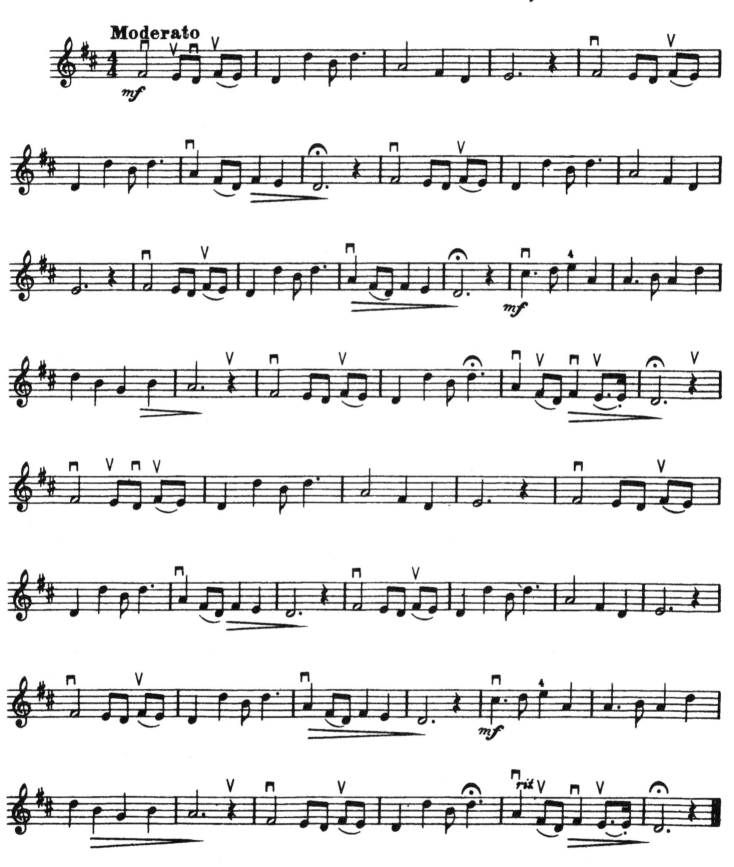

O Sanctissima
(O Thou Joyful Day)

VIOLIN

Latin hymn A.D. 1500
Folk-song of the Sicilian Seas
F. GRÜBER

Arr. by EDWARD STRIETEL

Rock of Ages

VIOLIN

THOMAS HASTINGS
Arr. by EDWARD STRIETEL

Santa Lucia

VIOLIN

Neapolitan Boat Song
Arr. by C. Paul Herfurth

Silent Night, Holy Night

VIOLIN

FRANZ GRÜBER
(1818)
Arr. by EDWARD STRIETEL

W.M.Co. 5744-Comp.

The Star-Spangled Banner

THE NATIONAL ANTHEM
Written during the war of 1812

Melody "To Anacreon in Heaven"
By JOHN STAFFORD SMITH (1750-1836)
Arr. by EDWARD STRIETEL

VIOLIN

W. M. Co. 5744 - Comp.

Silver Threads among the Gold

VIOLIN

H. P. DANKS
(1834-1903)
Arr. by C. Paul Herfurth

W. M. Co. 5744-Comp.

Songs My Mother Taught Me

VIOLIN

ANTON DVOŘÁK
(1841-1904)
Arr. by C. Paul Herfurth

Copyright *MCMXXXVI,* by *The Willis Music Co.*

Song of the Volga Boatmen

VIOLIN

Russian Folk-song
Arr. by C. Paul Herfurth

W. M. Co. 5744 - Comp

Turkey in the Straw

VIOLIN

American Folk-tune
Arr. by C. Paul Herfurth

Wearing of the Green

An old revolutionary street ballad
used in the play, "Arrah na Pogue"

DION BOUCICAULT
Arr. by EDWARD STRIETEL

VIOLIN

W. M. Co. 5744-Comp.

Yankee Doodle

During the Revolutionary War this
song was used by the British to make
fun of the Yankees and later by the Yankees to taunt the British.

Source unknown
Arr. by EDWARD STRIETEL

VIOLIN

W.M. Co. 5744 - Comp.